Donated in remembrance of

[illegible] Palumbo

1962–2017

By

The Housman Family

20

"The love of learning, the sequestered nook, & all the sweet serenity of books."

~Henry Wadsworth Longfellow